Language Development Lessons for Early Childhood

Jean Gilliam DeGaetano
Illustrated by Kevin M. Newman

Great Ideas for Teaching, Inc. • P.O. Box 444 • Wrightsville Beach, NC 28480-0444

ISBN 1-886143-43-9

Language Development Lessons for Early Childhood

By Jean Gilliam DeGaetano
Illustrations by Kevin M. Newman

The purpose of these lessons is to strengthen listening skills and to provide various methods to encourage young learners to answer questions orally and to enjoy communicating with others.

The questions incorporate three basic techniques that encourage children to interact with a speaker.

Yes or No Answers:

For the reluctant talker, saying <u>yes</u> or <u>no</u> or shaking the head will let the professional know if the child is comprehending the questions.

Choosing Between Two Answers:

For shy children or children who have difficulty with word-retrieval, choosing between answers they hear eliminates the problem of knowing the answer but being unable to retrieve it from memory. This type of practice seems to improve the child's ability to recall answers.

Completing Sentences:

For children who need practice in using inferences and associations to improve word retrieval skills, sentence completion activities play a valuable role.

While one technique may work better than others, all three are excellent practice in stimulating receptive and expressive language in young children.

The activities in each lesson provide the structured method and repetitious practice needed to master these skills.

Each lesson has a student worksheet and three lesson plans. All four sheets should be reproduced and stored together as a unit. For students who are only able to do one lesson each day, it may be necessary to make three copies of the student worksheet so that one will be available for each lesson.

Name: _____

Date: _____

Language Development Lessons for
Early Childhood

Great Ideas for Teaching, Inc.

Instructor's Worksheet

<u>DIRECTIONS:</u> Before beginning, each student should be given a copy of the student worksheet that corresponds to the instructor's worksheet. Students should look at the large picture as the instructor reads each question aloud. The questions only require a <u>yes</u> or <u>no</u> answer. Some students may choose to verbalize more details. Non-verbal students may answer through their individual methods of indicating yes or no.

1. Is the girl wearing a skirt?

2. Does she have black hair?

3. Is the boy wearing shorts?

4. Does the boy have freckles on his face?

5. Is the girl mowing the grass?

6. Is the girl holding a watering can?

7. Is the boy mowing the grass with a tractor?

8. Is the boy pushing the lawn mower?

9. Are there three flowers in the picture?

10. Will the boy cut down the flowers?

Instructor's Worksheet

<u>DIRECTIONS:</u> Before beginning, each student should be given a copy of the student worksheet that corresponds to the instructor's worksheet. Students should look at the large picture as the instructor reads each question aloud. Each question includes a choice of two answers. This method of questioning only requires recognizing the correct answer and repeating it. It is excellent practice for developing skills in answering questions.

1. Is the girl wearing pants or a skirt?

2. Does she have blonde hair or black hair?

3. Is the boy wearing pants or shorts?

4. Does his shirt have stripes on it or polka-dots?

5. Is the girl or the boy mowing the grass?

6. Is the girl holding a watering can or a bottle?

7. Do the daisies have a couple of petals or many petals?

8. Is the boy pushing or pulling the lawn mower?

9. Does the lawn mower have big wheels or little wheels?

10. Is the boy mowing the grass or mowing the flowers?

Instructor's Worksheet   Completing Sentences

DIRECTIONS: Before beginning, each student should be given a copy of the student worksheet that corresponds to the instructor's worksheet. Students should look at the large picture as the instructor reads each statement aloud. The method of answering is to complete each statement with an appropriate word. This skill incorporates good listening, comprehending, making inferences and associations and using these skills to retrieve an appropriate word. Answers may not always be the same but are correct if they complete an accurate statement.

1. The girl is holding a _____.

2. The can is full of _____.

3. She is pouring water on the _____.

4. The boy is cutting the _____.

5. He is using a _____.

6. He should be careful not to cut the three _____.

7. A lawn mower rolls on four _____.

8. Water is coming out of the holes in the _____.

9. The blades in a lawn mower are very _____.

10. When the boy uses the lawn mower, he needs to be very _____.

Language Development Lessons for Early Childhood

Name: ______________________________ Date: ______________

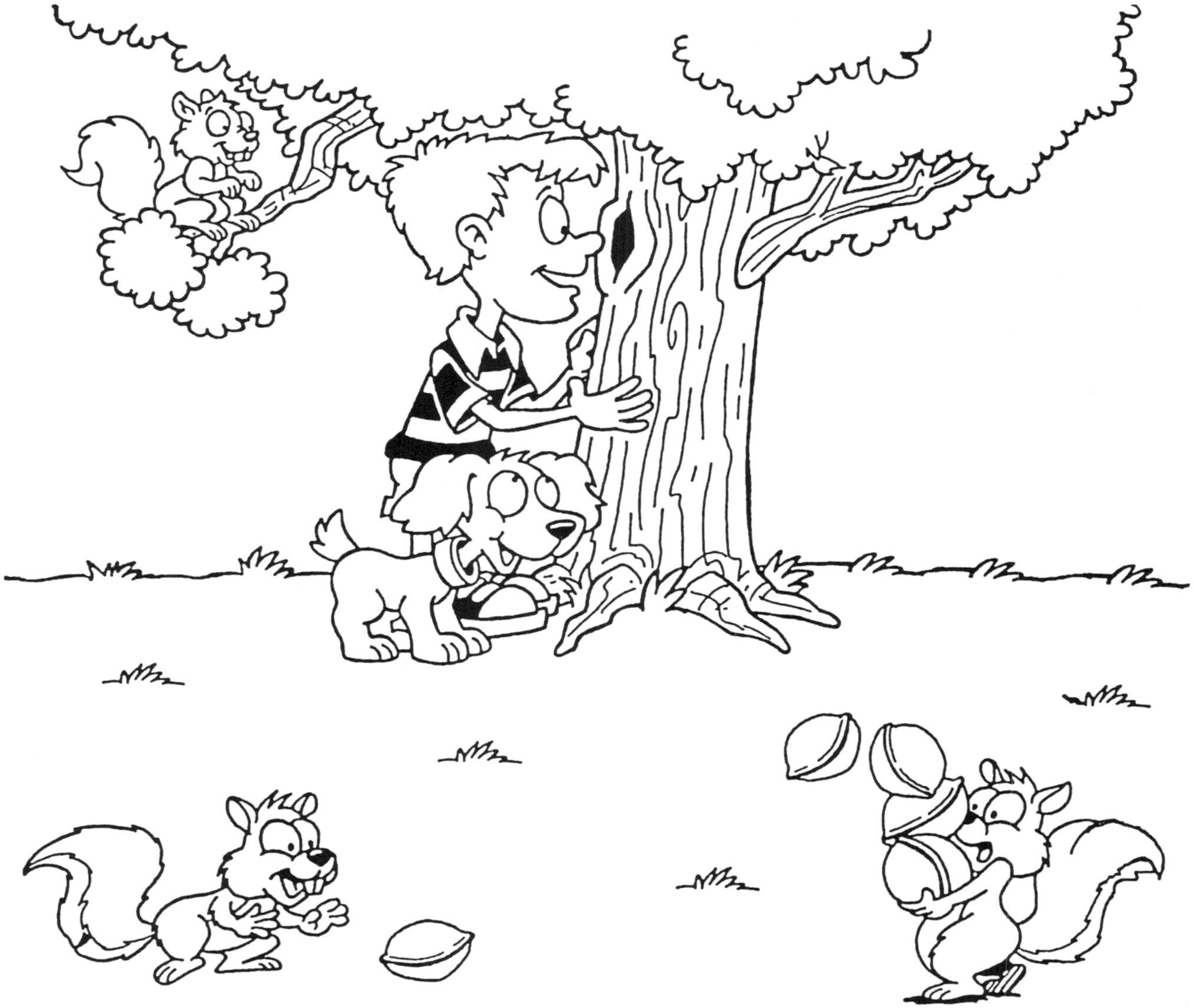

Instructor's Worksheet

Yes or No Answers

DIRECTIONS: Before beginning, each student should be given a copy of the student worksheet that corresponds to the instructor's worksheet. Students should look at the large picture as the instructor reads each question aloud. The questions only require a <u>yes</u> or <u>no</u> answer. Some students may choose to verbalize more details. Non-verbal students may answer through their individual methods of indicating yes or no.

1. Do you see three squirrels in the picture?

2. Are the squirrels gathering strawberries?

3. Is the dog looking in a hole?

4. Does the tree have branches?

5. Is the dog standing beside the boy?

6. Does the dog look like it is barking?

7. Is one squirrel dropping some of the nuts?

8. Do you see any birds in the tree?

9. Can the dog climb the tree?

10. Do you see lots of leaves in the picture?

Instructor's Worksheet

Choosing Between Two Answers

<u>DIRECTIONS:</u> Before beginning, each student should be given a copy of the student worksheet that corresponds to the instructor's worksheet. Students should look at the large picture as the instructor reads each question aloud. Each question includes a choice of two answers. This method of questioning only requires recognizing the correct answer and repeating it. It is excellent practice for developing skills in answering questions.

1. Do you see four squirrels or three squirrels in the picture?

2. Are the squirrels gathering nuts or strawberries?

3. Is the boy looking in the leaves or in a hole in the tree?

4. Is the puppy looking in the hole or looking at the boy?

5. Does the tree have branches or arms?

6. Does the boy have on a striped shirt or a polka-dotted shirt?

7. Is the squirrel in the tree watching the boy or the other squirrels?

8. Does the dog have a collar or a necklace around its neck?

9. Does the dog have a long tail or a short tail?

10. Is the tree big or little?

Language Development Lessons for
Early Childhood

DIRECTIONS: Before beginning, each student should be given a copy of the student worksheet that corresponds to the instructor's worksheet. Students should look at the large picture as the instructor reads each statement aloud. The method of answering is to complete each statement with an appropriate word. This skill incorporates good listening, comprehending, making inferences and associations and using these skills to retrieve an appropriate word. Answers may not always be the same but are correct if they complete an accurate statement.

1. The boy is looking in a _____.

2. The dog is standing beside the _____.

3. On the tree limb, I see a _____.

4. One squirrel is dropping a _____.

5. The boy is wearing a striped _____.

6. Both of the boy's hands are on the _____.

7. I know it is summertime because the tree has _____.

8. I know the boy is happy because he is _____.

9. The dog is not tall enough to peek in the _____.

10. I think the boy is looking for a _____.

Name: _____

SCHOOL

Instructor's Worksheet

Yes or No Answers

DIRECTIONS: Before beginning, each student should be given a copy of the student worksheet that corresponds to the instructor's worksheet. Students should look at the large picture as the instructor reads each question aloud. The questions only require a yes or no answer. Some students may choose to verbalize more details. Non-verbal students may answer through their individual methods of indicating yes or no.

1. Are the girls walking to school?

2. Are they wearing coats?

3. Are both girls wearing backpacks?

4. Is one girl carrying a lunch box?

5. Does one girl have her hair in a ponytail?

6. Do you see big trees in the picture?

7. Do you see birds in the picture?

8. Is it a rainy day?

9. Are the girls walking in the street?

10. Are the girls walking on a sidewalk?

Language Development Lessons for
Early Childhood

Instructor's Worksheet

Choosing Between Two Answers

<u>DIRECTIONS:</u> Before beginning, each student should be given a copy of the student worksheet that corresponds to the instructor's worksheet. Students should look at the large picture as the instructor reads each question aloud. Each question includes a choice of two answers. This method of questioning only requires recognizing the correct answer and repeating it. It is excellent practice for developing skills in answering questions.

1. Do you see two or three girls?

2. Are the girls walking or running?

3. Do you see a school or a fire station?

4. Is the girl who is closest to the school wearing a dress or shorts?

5. Is the bird on the fence flapping its wings or sitting still?

6. In the picture, do you see trees or bushes?

7. Are the girls walking on a street or on a sidewalk?

8. Who will arrive at the school first, the girl with the ponytail or the girl with straight hair?

9. Are the girls wearing boots or shoes?

10. Do you think it is summertime or wintertime?

Language Development Lessons for
Early Childhood

Instructor's Worksheet

Completing Sentences

<u>DIRECTIONS:</u> Before beginning, each student should be given a copy of the student worksheet that corresponds to the instructor's worksheet. Students should look at the large picture as the instructor reads each statement aloud. The method of answering is to complete each statement with an appropriate word. This skill incorporates good listening, comprehending, making inferences and associations and using these skills to retrieve an appropriate word. Answers may not always be the same but are correct if they complete an accurate statement.

1. The girls are going to _____.

2. They are walking on a _____.

3. On their feet they have _____.

4. I don't see trees but I do see _____.

5. One girl is holding the straps of her _____.

6. The other girl is holding the handle of her _____.

7. One girl has on a dress and the other girl has on _____.

8. One bird is flapping its _____.

9. The other bird is standing on the _____.

10. The school has doors and _____.

Language Development Lessons for
Early Childhood

Name: _____

Date: _____

Great Ideas for Teaching, Inc.

Language Development Lessons for
Early Childhood

Instructor's Worksheet

Yes or No Answers

DIRECTIONS: Before beginning, each student should be given a copy of the student worksheet that corresponds to the instructor's worksheet. Students should look at the large picture as the instructor reads each question aloud. The questions only require a yes or no answer. Some students may choose to verbalize more details. Non-verbal students may answer through their individual methods of indicating yes or no.

1. Is the girl riding a two-wheeler?

2. Is the boy bouncing on a pogo stick?

3. Are the children playing on a sidewalk?

4. Is the sidewalk made of sticks?

5. Are both children moving in the same direction?

6. Are the children wearing winter clothes?

7. Is the girl wearing a striped shirt?

8. Is the girl's hair longer than the boy's hair?

9. Do you see a squirrel in the picture?

10. Does the squirrel have a thin tail?

Language Development Lessons for
Early Childhood

Instructor's Worksheet

Choosing Between Two Answers

1. Is the girl riding a bicycle or a tricycle?

2. Is the boy playing with a skateboard or a pogo stick?

3. Are the children playing on a sidewalk or on a road?

4. Is the sidewalk made of sticks or concrete?

5. Is the boy hopping or rolling on the pogo stick?

6. Are the children wearing sneakers or sandals?

7. Is the boy wearing a striped shirt or a checkered shirt?

8. Is the girl's hair longer or shorter than the boy's hair?

9. Does the squirrel have a thin tail or a fluffy tail?

10. Does the branch have leaves or flowers?

Instructor's Worksheet   Completing Sentences

<u>DIRECTIONS:</u> Before beginning, each student should be given a copy of the student worksheet that corresponds to the instructor's worksheet. Students should look at the large picture as the instructor reads each statement aloud. The method of answering is to complete each statement with an appropriate word. This skill incorporates good listening, comprehending, making inferences and associations and using these skills to retrieve an appropriate word. Answers may not always be the same but are correct if they complete an accurate statement.

1. The boy is bouncing on a _____.

2. He is wearing a striped _____.

3. On his feet he has _____.

4. The girl is riding a _____.

5. The tricycle has three _____.

6. She is holding the _____.

7. Her feet are on the _____.

8. I can see the trunk and roots of a big _____.

9. A squirrel is sitting on one of the tree _____.

10. They are not riding on a road but are playing on a _____.

Name: _____

Date: _____

Instructor's Worksheet

DIRECTIONS: Before beginning, each student should be given a copy of the student worksheet that corresponds to the instructor's worksheet. Students should look at the large picture as the instructor reads each question aloud. The questions only require a _yes_ or _no_ answer. Some students may choose to verbalize more details. Non-verbal students may answer through their individual methods of indicating yes or no.

1. Is the boy skiing?

2. Is he on the sled alone?

3. Does the boy have on warm clothing?

4. Does the sled have wheels?

5. Does the sled have runners?

6. Is it snowing in the picture?

7. Do you see snow on the trees?

8. Do you think it is warm outside?

9. Does the boy have on ice skates?

10. Is the dog wearing a collar around its neck?

Instructor's Worksheet

Choosing Between Two Answers

<u>DIRECTIONS:</u> Before beginning, each student should be given a copy of the student worksheet that corresponds to the instructor's worksheet. Students should look at the large picture as the instructor reads each question aloud. Each question includes a choice of two answers. This method of questioning only requires recognizing the correct answer and repeating it. It is excellent practice for developing skills in answering questions.

1. Is the boy skiing or sledding?

2. Is he riding the sled with a cat or a dog?

3. Does the boy have on warm clothes or cool clothes?

4. Does the sled have wheels or runners?

5. Is it raining or snowing in the picture?

6. Do you see snow or rain on the trees?

7. Do you think it is warm or cold outside?

8. Is the boy going up or down the hill?

9. Does the dog look frightened or happy?

10. Is the snow hot or cold?

Language Development Lessons for
Early Childhood

Instructor's Worksheet   Completing Sentences

<u>DIRECTIONS:</u> Before beginning, each student should be given a copy of the student worksheet that corresponds to the instructor's worksheet. Students should look at the large picture as the instructor reads each statement aloud. The method of answering is to complete each statement with an appropriate word. This skill incorporates good listening, comprehending, making inferences and associations and using these skills to retrieve an appropriate word. Answers may not always be the same but are correct if they complete an accurate statement.

1. The boy is on a _____.

2. The weather is _____.

3. The sled is sliding on the _____.

4. The trees are covered in _____.

5. In the air I see _____.

6. The boy is riding with his _____.

7. The boy has a cap on his _____.

8. He has a scarf around his _____.

9. A sled does not have wheels. It has _____.

10. The boy is holding the rope in his _____.

Name: ______________________ Date: ______________

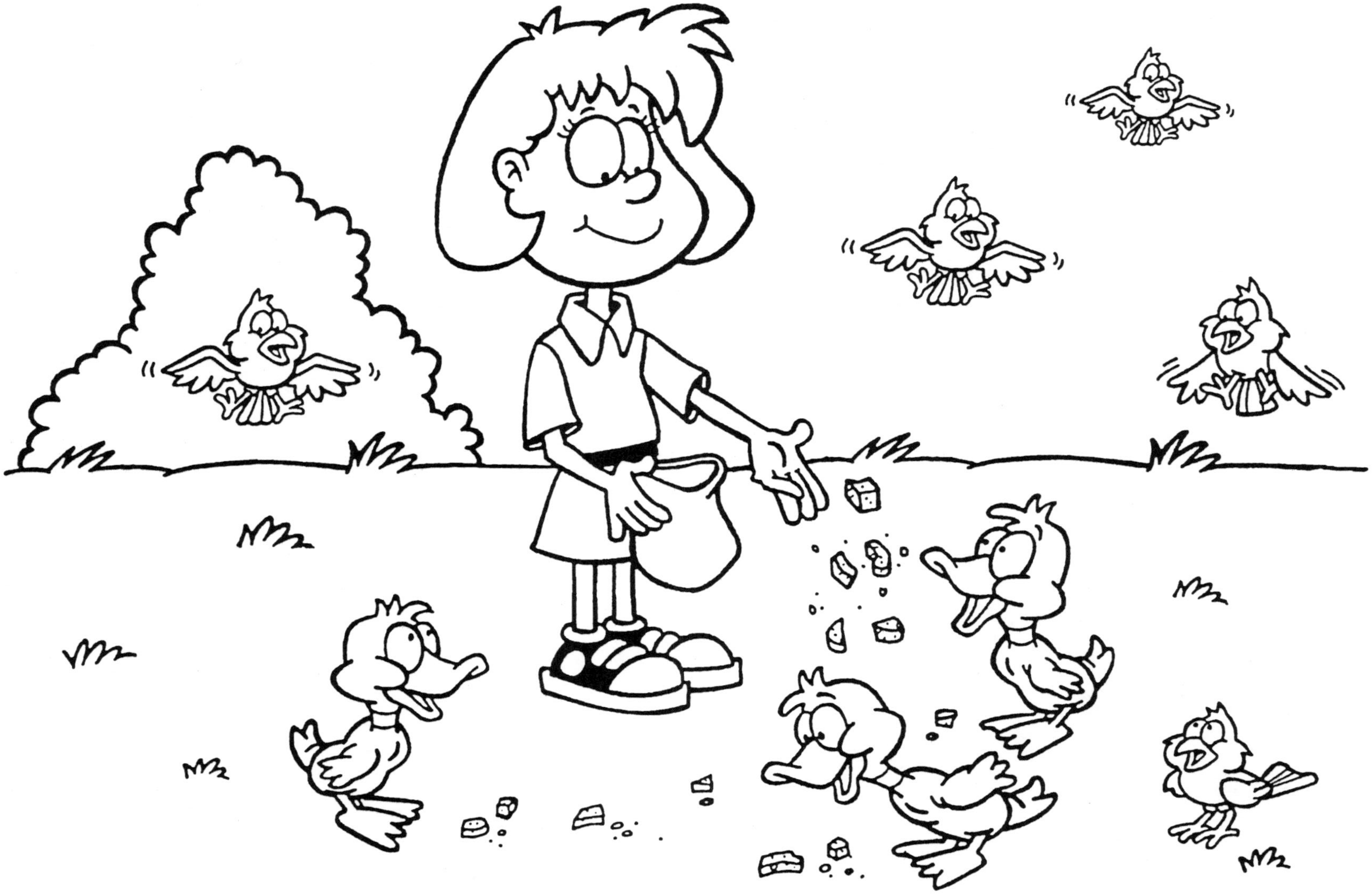

Instructor's Worksheet

Yes or No Answers

DIRECTIONS: Before beginning, each student should be given a copy of the student worksheet that corresponds to the instructor's worksheet. Students should look at the large picture as the instructor reads each question aloud. The questions only require a yes or no answer. Some students may choose to verbalize more details. Non-verbal students may answer through their individual methods of indicating yes or no.

1. Is the girl feeding roosters?

2. Is she giving the ducks bread crumbs?

3. Are all the birds flying?

4. Do you think the birds would like to have some bread crumbs?

5. Do birds have feathers?

6. Do ducks have feathers?

7. Does the girl have the bread crumbs in a jar?

8. Does a bird's foot look like a duck's foot?

9. Do the ducks have larger feet than the birds?

10. Are the ducks afraid of the girl?

Language Development Lessons for
Early Childhood

Instructor's Worksheet   Choosing Between Two Answers

DIRECTIONS: Before beginning, each student should be given a copy of the student worksheet that corresponds to the instructor's worksheet. Students should look at the large picture as the instructor reads each question aloud. Each question includes a choice of two answers. This method of questioning only requires recognizing the correct answer and repeating it. It is excellent practice for developing skills in answering questions.

1. Is there a girl or a boy in the picture?

2. Is she a baby or a big girl?

3. Is she feeding roosters or ducks?

4. Is she feeding the ducks bread crumbs or pickles?

5. Are most of the birds flying in the air or sitting on the ground?

6. Do you think birds prefer to eat bread crumbs or lemons?

7. Do birds have feathers or fur?

8. Do ducks have feathers or scales?

9. Does the girl have bread crumbs in a bag or in a jar?

10. Is the girl happy or sad?

Instructor's Worksheet   Completing Sentences

DIRECTIONS: Before beginning, each student should be given a copy of the student worksheet that corresponds to the instructor's worksheet. Students should look at the large picture as the instructor reads each statement aloud. The method of answering is to complete each statement with an appropriate word. This skill incorporates good listening, comprehending, making inferences and associations and using these skills to retrieve an appropriate word. Answers may not always be the same but are correct if they complete an accurate statement.

1. The girl has the bread crumbs in a _____.

2. She is tossing the crumbs to the _____.

3. Five birds hope she will give them some _____.

4. She tosses the bread crumbs with her _____.

5. The ducks are not afraid of the _____.

6. One bird is on the ground. The others are _____.

7. Ducks have webbed _____.

8. Both birds and ducks are covered in _____.

9. The ducks pick up the bread crumbs with their _____.

10. People have arms. Ducks and birds have _____.

Language Development Lessons for
Early Childhood

Name: _____

Instructor's Worksheet   Yes or No Answers

DIRECTIONS: Before beginning, each student should be given a copy of the student worksheet that corresponds to the instructor's worksheet. Students should look at the large picture as the instructor reads each question aloud. The questions only require a <u>yes</u> or <u>no</u> answer. Some students may choose to verbalize more details. Non-verbal students may answer through their individual methods of indicating yes or no.

1. Are the children feeding ducks?

2. Are two birds standing on the ground?

3. Are other birds joining the two on the ground?

4. Do the children have on boots?

5. Are two birds sitting on the back of the bench?

6. Do both children have food for the birds?

7. Is the boy sitting on a swing?

8. Is the bench larger than a bird?

9. Is the girl's hair the same color as the boy's hair?

10. Are the children's food bags the same shape?

Instructor's Worksheet

<u>DIRECTIONS:</u> Before beginning, each student should be given a copy of the student worksheet that corresponds to the instructor's worksheet. Students should look at the large picture as the instructor reads each question aloud. Each question includes a choice of two answers. This method of questioning only requires recognizing the correct answer and repeating it. It is excellent practice for developing skills in answering questions.

1. Do you see grownups or children in the picture?

2. Are they feeding ducks or birds?

3. Are there two birds or three birds on the ground?

4. Does the girl have on a short-sleeved shirt or a long-sleeved shirt?

5. Do the children have on sneakers or boots?

6. Is the boy sitting on a bench or a swing?

7. Are they feeding the birds bread or giving them a drink of water?

8. Are they putting the bread in a dish or tossing it on the ground?

9. Do you see birds or airplanes in the sky?

10. Do you think the children will take the birds home or leave them in the park?

Instructor's Worksheet

Completing Sentences

DIRECTIONS: Before beginning, each student should be given a copy of the student worksheet that corresponds to the instructor's worksheet. Students should look at the large picture as the instructor reads each statement aloud. The method of answering is to complete each statement with an appropriate word. This skill incorporates good listening, comprehending, making inferences and associations and using these skills to retrieve an appropriate word. Answers may not always be the same but are correct if they complete an accurate statement.

1. The children are feeding the _____.

2. They are feeding them _____.

3. They have their bread crumbs in _____.

4. They are tossing the bread crumbs on the _____.

5. In all, there are four _____.

6. The boy brought along his round, rubber _____.

7. Both children are wearing socks and _____.

8. In the sky, I see two clouds and two _____.

9. The tiny ladybug has round, black _____.

10. The hungry birds will eat the _____.

Language Development Lessons for
Early Childhood

Name: ______________________ Date: ______________

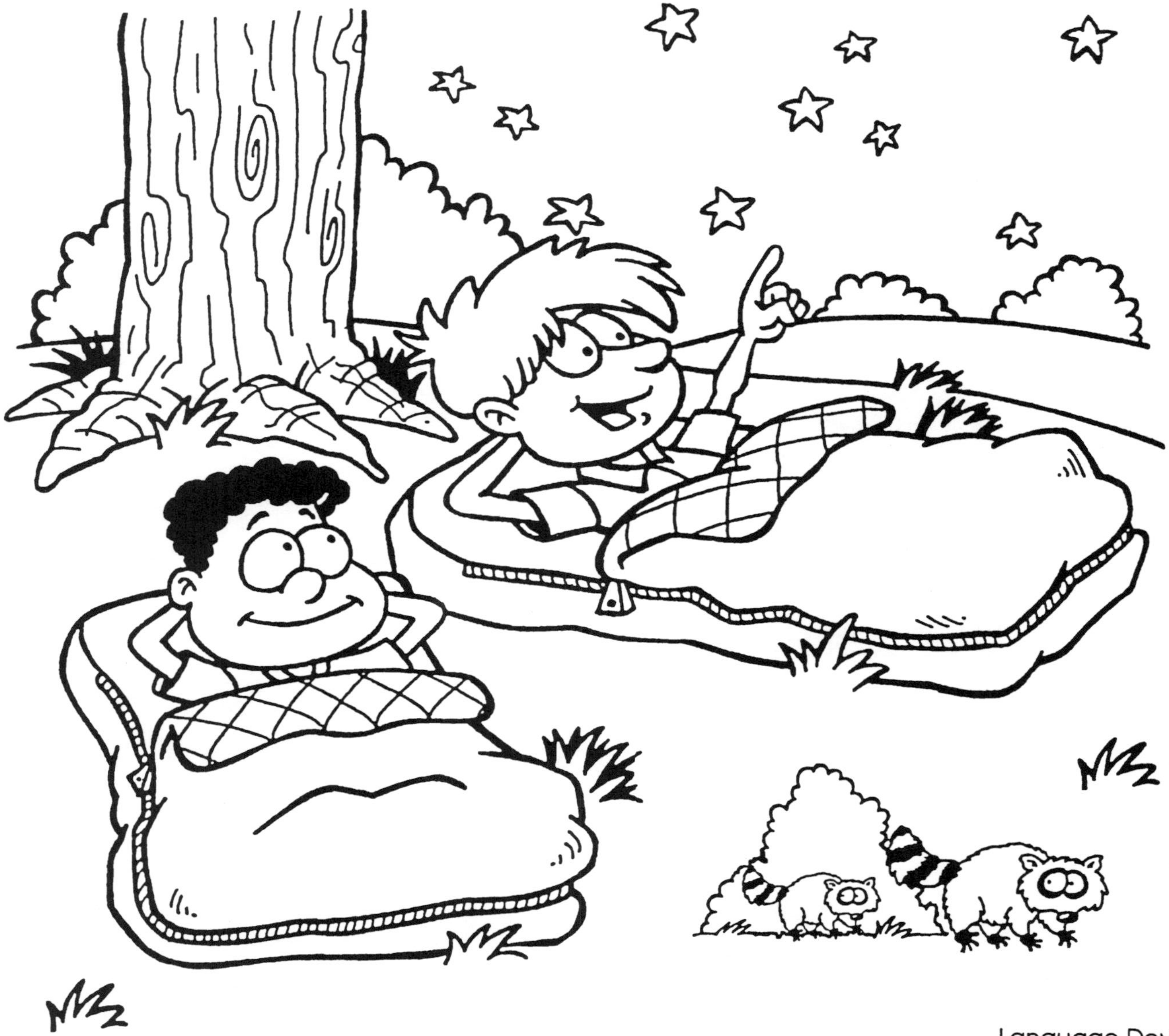

Instructor's Worksheet

Yes or No Answers

DIRECTIONS: Before beginning, each student should be given a copy of the student worksheet that corresponds to the instructor's worksheet. Students should look at the large picture as the instructor reads each question aloud. The questions only require a <u>yes</u> or <u>no</u> answer. Some students may choose to verbalize more details. Non-verbal students may answer through their individual methods of indicating yes or no.

1. Do you see the moon in the sky?

2. Are the boys sleeping in tents?

3. Do sleeping bags have zippers?

4. Are sleeping bags made of glass?

5. Are sleeping bags warm?

6. Are sleeping bags soft?

7. Do you see raccoons in the picture?

8. Do the children see the animals?

9. Are the children sleeping?

10. Is the boy with black hair listening to the other boy?

Language Development Lessons for
Early Childhood

Instructor's Worksheet

Choosing Between Two Answers

DIRECTIONS: Before beginning, each student should be given a copy of the student worksheet that corresponds to the instructor's worksheet. Students should look at the large picture as the instructor reads each question aloud. Each question includes a choice of two answers. This method of questioning only requires recognizing the correct answer and repeating it. It is excellent practice for developing skills in answering questions.

1. Do you see stars or the sun in the sky?

2. Are the boys sleeping in tents or in sleeping bags?

3. Do the sleeping bags have zippers or buttons?

4. Are sleeping bags made of glass or cloth?

5. Are they sleeping inside or outside a house?

6. Do you think the sleeping bags are warm or cold?

7. Do you see rabbits or raccoons in the picture?

8. Are the children awake or asleep?

9. Is the boy pointing towards the raccoons or the stars?

10. Are the sleeping bags hard or soft?

Language Development Lessons for
Early Childhood

Instructor's Worksheet

Completing Sentences

DIRECTIONS: Before beginning, each student should be given a copy of the student worksheet that corresponds to the instructor's worksheet. Students should look at the large picture as the instructor reads each statement aloud. The method of answering is to complete each statement with an appropriate word. This skill incorporates good listening, comprehending, making inferences and associations and using these skills to retrieve an appropriate word. Answers may not always be the same but are correct if they complete an accurate statement.

1. The boys are in their _____.

2. The sleeping bags close with _____.

3. They should not get cold because sleeping bags are very _____.

4. Stars are shining in the _____.

5. The little animals are _____.

6. Usually the boys sleep in their _____.

7. The ground is hard but the sleeping bags are _____.

8. The boy is pointing at the _____.

9. They do not see the little _____.

10. One boy is talking. The other boy is _____.

Name: _____

Date: _____

Instructor's Worksheet

Yes or No Answers

Before beginning, each student should be given a copy of the student worksheet that corresponds to the instructor's worksheet. Students should look at the large picture as the instructor reads each question aloud. The questions only require a <u>yes</u> or <u>no</u> answer. Some students may choose to verbalize more details. Non-verbal students may answer through their individual methods of indicating yes or no.

1. Do both girls have black hair?

2. Is one girl walking on stilts?

3. Are the stilts made of wood?

4. Is the girl standing on the swing?

5. Is there more than one swing in the picture?

6. Is the girl on the swing wearing a skirt?

7. Is the girl on the stilts wearing a skirt?

8. Is it a sunny day?

9. Do you think it is wintertime?

10. Is the dog wearing a collar?

Instructor's Worksheet   Choosing Between Two Answers

DIRECTIONS: Before beginning, each student should be given a copy of the student worksheet that corresponds to the instructor's worksheet. Students should look at the large picture as the instructor reads each question aloud. Each question includes a choice of two answers. This method of questioning only requires recognizing the correct answer and repeating it. It is excellent practice for developing skills in answering questions.

1. Do you see girls or boys in the picture?

2. Is one girl using a pogo stick or stilts?

3. Are the stilts made of wood or clay?

4. Is the girl standing or sitting on the swing?

5. Is she sitting still or swinging high?

6. Do you see one or two swings on the swing set?

7. Is there a cat or a dog in the picture?

8. Do you see a sun or a moon in the picture?

9. Do you think it is summertime or wintertime?

10. Is the dog wearing a collar or a leash?

Instructor's Worksheet

Completing Sentences

DIRECTIONS: Before beginning, each student should be given a copy of the student worksheet that corresponds to the instructor's worksheet. Students should look at the large picture as the instructor reads each statement aloud. The method of answering is to complete each statement with an appropriate word. This skill incorporates good listening, comprehending, making inferences and associations and using these skills to retrieve an appropriate word. Answers may not always be the same but are correct if they complete an accurate statement.

1. One girl is sitting on a _____.

2. The seat of the swing is hanging on _____.

3. The girl on the swing is holding the _____.

4. The other girl is walking on _____.

5. The stilts are made of _____.

6. Her feet are not touching the _____.

7. It is a warm, sunny _____.

8. The dog is wearing a _____.

9. Both girls are wearing sneakers on their _____.

10. One girl is sitting. The other is _____.

Name: _____

Date: _____

Language Development Lessons for Early Childhood

Great Ideas for Teaching, Inc.

Instructor's Worksheet

Yes or No Answers

DIRECTIONS: Before beginning, each student should be given a copy of the student worksheet that corresponds to the instructor's worksheet. Students should look at the large picture as the instructor reads each question aloud. The questions only require a <u>yes</u> or <u>no</u> answer. Some students may choose to verbalize more details. Non-verbal students may answer through their individual methods of indicating yes or no.

1. Are a few snowflakes still falling?

2. Do you see a snowman in the picture?

3. Is the snowman holding a rake?

4. Is the snowman wearing a scarf?

5. Is the girl using a big shovel?

6. Is the boy sliding on a sled?

7. Does the sled have runners?

8. Is it raining in the picture?

9. Is the girl's fort made of bricks?

10. Do you think the fort will melt when the sun comes out?

Instructor's Worksheet

Choosing Between Two Answers

DIRECTIONS: Before beginning, each student should be given a copy of the student worksheet that corresponds to the instructor's worksheet. Students should look at the large picture as the instructor reads each question aloud. Each question includes a choice of two answers. This method of questioning only requires recognizing the correct answer and repeating it. It is excellent practice for developing skills in answering questions.

1. Do you see a snowman or a snowmobile in the picture?

2. Is the snowman holding a rake or a broom?

3. Is the snowman wearing a scarf or a hat?

4. Did the girl make some snowballs or cotton balls?

5. Is the girl wearing a hat or a hood?

6. Is the boy riding a sled or a snowmobile?

7. Does the sled have wheels or runners?

8. Is the sled going down the hill or up the hill?

9. Is the girl's fort made of bricks or snow?

10. Do you think the fort will melt or freeze if the sun comes out?

Language Development Lessons for
Early Childhood

Instructor's Worksheet

Completing Sentences

DIRECTIONS: Before beginning, each student should be given a copy of the student worksheet that corresponds to the instructor's worksheet. Students should look at the large picture as the instructor reads each statement aloud. The method of answering is to complete each statement with an appropriate word. This skill incorporates good listening, comprehending, making inferences and associations and using these skills to retrieve an appropriate word. Answers may not always be the same but are correct if they complete an accurate statement.

1. The boy is on a _____.

2. The girl is building a _____.

3. She is patting the snow down with a _____.

4. She made some round _____.

5. A few snowflakes are still _____.

6. The snowman is holding a _____.

7. On their heads, both children are wearing _____.

8. When the sun comes out, the snowman will _____.

9. The trees are covered with _____.

10. The girl has a scarf around her _____.

Name: ______________________ Date: ______________

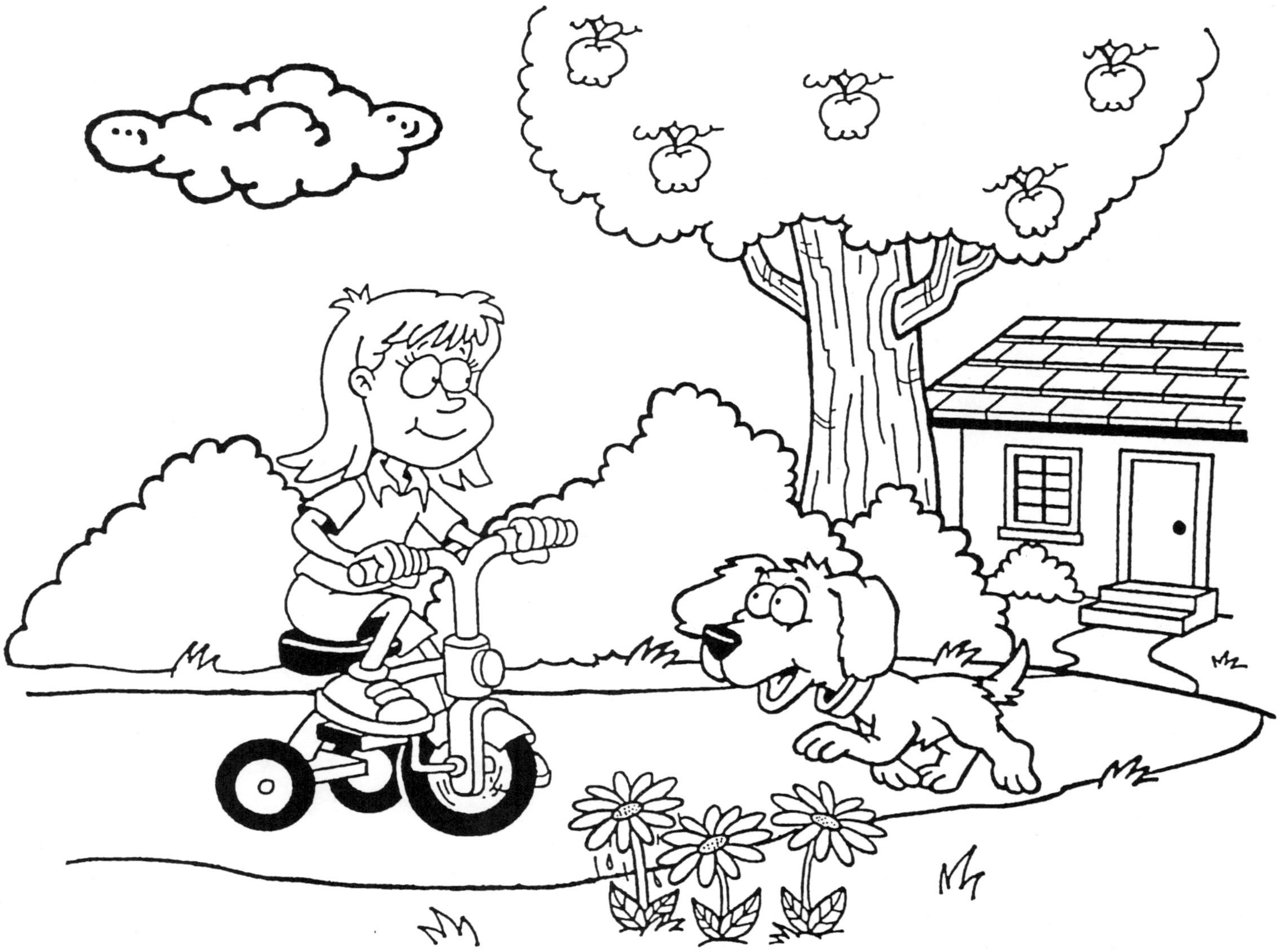

Instructor's Worksheet

Yes or No Answers

DIRECTIONS: Before beginning, each student should be given a copy of the student worksheet that corresponds to the instructor's worksheet. Students should look at the large picture as the instructor reads each question aloud. The questions only require a <u>yes</u> or <u>no</u> answer. Some students may choose to verbalize more details. Non-verbal students may answer through their individual methods of indicating yes or no.

1. Is the girl riding a tricycle?

2. Does the tricycle have four wheels?

3. Does she have on a coat?

4. Does her shirt have a collar?

5. Is the dog wearing a collar?

6. Is the dog wearing a leash?

7. Do you see apples on the tree?

8. Do you see a chimney on the house?

9. Do you see two windows on the house?

10. Is the door of the house closed?

Instructor's Worksheet

Choosing Between Two Answers

DIRECTIONS: Before beginning, each student should be given a copy of the student worksheet that corresponds to the instructor's worksheet. Students should look at the large picture as the instructor reads each question aloud. Each question includes a choice of two answers. This method of questioning only requires recognizing the correct answer and repeating it. It is excellent practice for developing skills in answering questions.

1. Do you see a young girl or a grandmother in the picture?

2. Is she riding a bicycle or a tricycle?

3. Does the tricycle have three wheels or two wheels?

4. Does the girl have on a shirt or a coat?

5. Does she have her hair in a ponytail or hanging down?

6. Is the dog wearing a collar or a bow?

7. Is the dog on a leash or walking by itself?

8. Do you see oranges or apples on the tree?

9. Do you see apples or flowers on the ground?

10. Is the door of the house open or closed?

Instructor's Worksheet   Completing Sentences

DIRECTIONS: Before beginning, each student should be given a copy of the student worksheet that corresponds to the instructor's worksheet. Students should look at the large picture as the instructor reads each statement aloud. The method of answering is to complete each statement with an appropriate word. This skill incorporates good listening, comprehending, making inferences and associations and using these skills to retrieve an appropriate word. Answers may not always be the same but are correct if they complete an accurate statement.

1. The girl is riding a _____.

2. A tricycle has three _____.

3. She is holding on to the _____.

4. Her dog is wearing a _____.

5. The girl and the dog live in the _____.

6. The tree in the yard has _____.

7. People have fingers and toes. Dogs have _____.

8. The girl has her feet on the tricycle _____.

9. There is a cloud in the _____.

10. If the girl shakes the tree, the apples may _____.

Language Development Lessons for
Early Childhood

Instructor's Worksheet

Yes or No Answers

<u>DIRECTIONS:</u> Before beginning, each student should be given a copy of the student worksheet that corresponds to the instructor's worksheet. Students should look at the large picture as the instructor reads each question aloud. The questions only require a <u>yes</u> or <u>no</u> answer. Some students may choose to verbalize more details. Non-verbal students may answer through their individual methods of indicating yes or no.

1. Do you see a girl?

2. Is she wearing a dress?

3. Is she walking on a sidewalk?

4. Is the girl wearing sneakers?

5. Do you see a lake?

6. Is the girl running?

7. Is the dog following her?

8. Is the dog wearing a collar around its neck?

9. Is the girl walking in the rain?

10. Do you see any trees in the background?

Instructor's Worksheet

Choosing Between Two Answers

DIRECTIONS: Before beginning, each student should be given a copy of the student worksheet that corresponds to the instructor's worksheet. Students should look at the large picture as the instructor reads each question aloud. Each question includes a choice of two answers. This method of questioning only requires recognizing the correct answer and repeating it. It is excellent practice for developing skills in answering questions.

1. Do you see a girl or a boy in the picture?

2. Is the girl wearing a dress or shorts?

3. Is the girl walking on a sidewalk or on the grass?

4. Is she walking at a shopping mall or in the woods?

5. Is the girl walking or running?

6. Is the girl walking with a dog or a deer?

7. Is the dog following the girl or leading her?

8. Is the dog wearing a collar or a scarf around its neck?

9. Is the dog walking or hopping?

10. Do you see leaves or apples on the trees?

Instructor's Worksheet

Completing Sentences

DIRECTIONS: Before beginning, each student should be given a copy of the student worksheet that corresponds to the instructor's worksheet. Students should look at the large picture as the instructor reads each statement aloud. The method of answering is to complete each statement with an appropriate word. This skill incorporates good listening, comprehending, making inferences and associations and using these skills to retrieve an appropriate word. Answers may not always be the same but are correct if they complete an accurate statement.

1. The girl is _____.

2. She is walking past three big _____.

3. Following her is her _____.

4. The dog is wearing a _____.

5. The girl is holding the straps of her _____.

6. She is wearing a shirt and _____.

7. The girl is walking on _____.

8. On her feet, she has _____.

9. I know she is enjoying herself because she is _____.

10. She has on short sleeves; therefore the weather must be _____.

Name: _____

Date: _____

Instructor's Worksheet

<u>DIRECTIONS:</u> Before beginning, each student should be given a copy of the student worksheet that corresponds to the instructor's worksheet. Students should look at the large picture as the instructor reads each question aloud. The questions only require a <u>yes</u> or <u>no</u> answer. Some students may choose to verbalize more details. Non-verbal students may answer through their individual methods of indicating yes or no.

1. Are there three children in the picture?

2. Is the boy carrying one box?

3. Is the girl carrying one box?

4. Is the girl carrying more boxes than the boy?

5. Are all of the girl's boxes big?

6. Do you see bows on any of the boxes?

7. Do all of the boxes have lids?

8. Is the window open?

9. Does the window have curtains?

10. Are the children outside?

Instructor's Worksheet

Choosing Between Two Answers

<u>DIRECTIONS:</u> Before beginning, each student should be given a copy of the student worksheet that corresponds to the instructor's worksheet. Students should look at the large picture as the instructor reads each question aloud. Each question includes a choice of two answers. This method of questioning only requires recognizing the correct answer and repeating it. It is excellent practice for developing skills in answering questions.

1. Are there three children or two children in the picture?

2. Is the boy carrying one box or two boxes?

3. Is the boy wearing sneakers or sandals?

4. Is the girl wearing a dress or pants?

5. Is she carrying the same number of boxes or more boxes than the boy?

6. Are the girl's boxes the same size or different sizes?

7. Do you see a door or a window in the picture?

8. Is the window open or closed?

9. Does the window have glass panes or a door knob?

10. Do you see curtains or blinds on the window?

Language Development Lessons for
Early Childhood

Instructor's Worksheet

Completing Sentences

<u>DIRECTIONS:</u> Before beginning, each student should be given a copy of the student worksheet that corresponds to the instructor's worksheet. Students should look at the large picture as the instructor reads each statement aloud. The method of answering is to complete each statement with an appropriate word. This skill incorporates good listening, comprehending, making inferences and associations and using these skills to retrieve an appropriate word. Answers may not always be the same but are correct if they complete an accurate statement.

1. The girl is carrying three _____.

2. The boy is carrying one _____.

3. There are three boxes on the _____.

4. Each box is covered with a _____.

5. The children are carrying the boxes in their _____.

6. The girl is carrying more boxes than the _____.

7. The window was closed but now it is _____.

8. The material hanging on the window is called _____.

9. If the children get cold, they will close the _____.

10. Both children are wearing socks and _____.

Name: _____

Before beginning, each student should be given a copy of the student worksheet that corresponds to the instructor's worksheet. Students should look at the large picture as the instructor reads each question aloud. The questions only require a yes or no answer. Some students may choose to verbalize more details. Non-verbal students may answer through their individual methods of indicating yes or no.

1. Is the girl standing in a pond?

2. Is her hair wet?

3. Are her clothes wet?

4. Does her shirt have a zipper?

5. Do you see the girl's shoes?

6. Is the frog wet?

7. Does the frog have spots on its body?

8. Do you think the girl's lunch might be in the bag?

9. Is the frog swimming in the water?

10. Do you think it is wintertime?

Instructor's Worksheet

Choosing Between Two Answers

DIRECTIONS: Before beginning, each student should be given a copy of the student worksheet that corresponds to the instructor's worksheet. Students should look at the large picture as the instructor reads each question aloud. Each question includes a choice of two answers. This method of questioning only requires recognizing the correct answer and repeating it. It is excellent practice for developing skills in answering questions.

1. Does the girl have long hair or short hair?

2. Are the girl's clothes wet or dry?

3. Does the girl have on a dress or shorts?

4. Does her shirt have buttons or a zipper?

5. Is the girl holding her shirt or her shorts?

6. Do you see a frog or a turtle in the picture?

7. Is the frog sitting on a log or a rock?

8. Does the frog have stripes or spots on its body?

9. Do you see a lunchbox or a lunch bag on the ground?

10. Do you think her lunch is wet or dry?

Language Development Lessons for
Early Childhood

Instructor's Worksheet   Completing Sentences

DIRECTIONS: Before beginning, each student should be given a copy of the student worksheet that corresponds to the instructor's worksheet. Students should look at the large picture as the instructor reads each statement aloud. The method of answering is to complete each statement with an appropriate word. This skill incorporates good listening, comprehending, making inferences and associations and using these skills to retrieve an appropriate word. Answers may not always be the same but are correct if they complete an accurate statement.

1. The girl was dry but now she is _____.

2. She is standing in a _____.

3. She is probably in the water because she _____.

4. She has her lunch in a paper _____.

5. Her shirt fastens together with _____.

6. The frog is sitting on a _____.

7. If she has on shoes, they are _____.

8. I can tell by her face that she is not _____.

9. It is summer so the weather is _____.

10. Frogs like to swim. That is why they live near _____.

Name: ______________________ Date: ______________

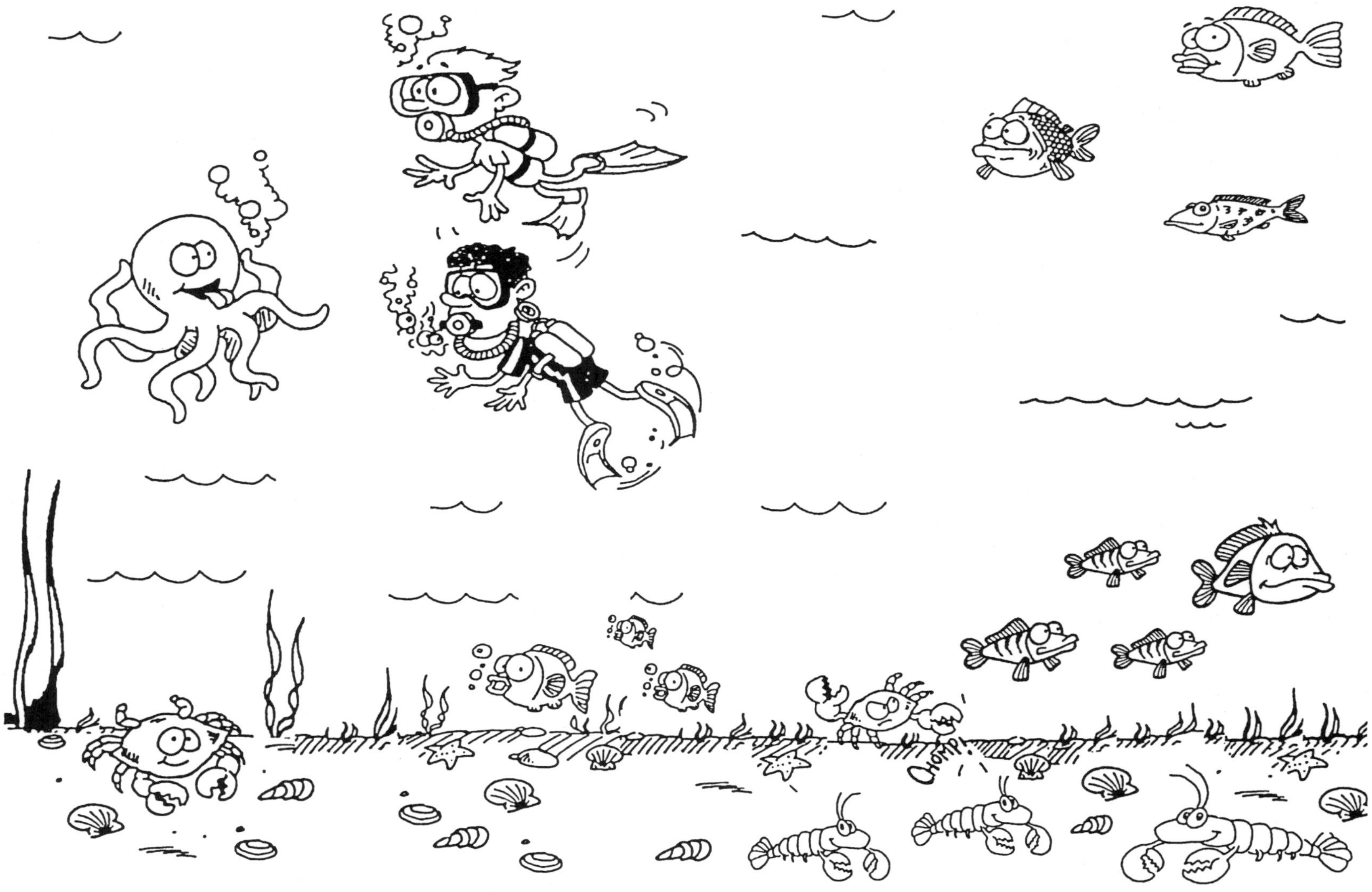

Instructor's Worksheet

Yes or No Answers

DIRECTIONS: Before beginning, each student should be given a copy of the student worksheet that corresponds to the instructor's worksheet. Students should look at the large picture as the instructor reads each question aloud. The questions only require a <u>yes</u> or <u>no</u> answer. Some students may choose to verbalize more details. Non-verbal students may answer through their individual methods of indicating yes or no.

1. Do you see divers in the picture?

2. Are they swimming on top of the water?

3. Do they have flippers on their feet?

4. Does the octopus have on flippers?

5. Do you see whales in the water?

6. Do you see seaweed on the bottom of the ocean?

7. Is the bottom of the ocean made of wood?

8. Do lobsters have fingers like people?

9. Are there more than four fish swimming in the water?

10. Do you think the water is frozen?

DIRECTIONS: Before beginning, each student should be given a copy of the student worksheet that corresponds to the instructor's worksheet. Students should look at the large picture as the instructor reads each question aloud. Each question includes a choice of two answers. This method of questioning only requires recognizing the correct answer and repeating it. It is excellent practice for developing skills in answering questions.

1. Do you see divers or mountain climbers in the picture?

2. Do they have on sunglasses or swim masks?

3. Do they have flippers on their hands or feet?

4. Are they looking at a porcupine or an octopus?

5. Do you see whales or smaller fish in the water?

6. Do you see seashells or pine cones on the sandy bottom?

7. Do you see seaweed or trees on the bottom of the ocean?

8. Do lobsters have fingers or claws?

9. Do crabs have flippers or pincers?

10. Do you see starfish or stars on the bottom of the ocean?

Instructor's Worksheet   Completing Sentences

DIRECTIONS: Before beginning, each student should be given a copy of the student worksheet that corresponds to the instructor's worksheet. Students should look at the large picture as the instructor reads each statement aloud. The method of answering is to complete each statement with an appropriate word. This skill incorporates good listening, comprehending, making inferences and associations and using these skills to retrieve an appropriate word. Answers may not always be the same but are correct if they complete an accurate statement.

1. The divers have flippers on their _____.

2. Their air tanks let them breathe under _____.

3. An octopus has eight _____.

4. Crabs and lobsters catch things with their _____.

5. The soft bottom on the ocean floor is made of _____.

6. The sea creature shaped like a star is called a _____.

7. Seashells are lying on the _____.

8. In the ocean, divers see many kinds of _____.

9. The grassy plants on the ocean bottom are called _____.

10. Fish can breathe in _____.

Language Development Lessons for
Early Childhood

Name: _____

Instructor's Worksheet

Yes or No Answers

DIRECTIONS: Before beginning, each student should be given a copy of the student worksheet that corresponds to the instructor's worksheet. Students should look at the large picture as the instructor reads each question aloud. The questions only require a _yes_ or _no_ answer. Some students may choose to verbalize more details. Non-verbal students may answer through their individual methods of indicating yes or no.

1. Do you see a girl in the picture?

2. Is the girl wearing a jacket?

3. Does her jacket have a zipper?

4. Do you see snowflakes falling?

5. Do the trees have leaves?

6. Is the wind blowing?

7. Do you see leaves blowing in the wind?

8. Do you see any birds on the ground?

9. Do you see a helicopter in the sky?

10. Do you see the moon behind the clouds?

Instructor's Worksheet

Choosing Between Two Answers

DIRECTIONS: Before beginning, each student should be given a copy of the student worksheet that corresponds to the instructor's worksheet. Students should look at the large picture as the instructor reads each question aloud. Each question includes a choice of two answers. This method of questioning only requires recognizing the correct answer and repeating it. It is excellent practice for developing skills in answering questions.

1. Is the girl wearing a long coat or a short jacket?

2. Does her jacket have buttons or a zipper?

3. Is she wearing pants or a skirt?

4. Is it a rainy day or a windy day?

5. Do you see leaves or snowflakes blowing in the wind?

6. Do the trees have leaves or bare branches?

7. Are the girl's hands in her pockets or out of her pockets?

8. Do you see birds or airplanes in the sky?

9. Do you see clouds or stars in the sky?

10. Do you see the sun or the moon peaking out behind the clouds?

Instructor's Worksheet   Completing Sentences

DIRECTIONS: Before beginning, each student should be given a copy of the student worksheet that corresponds to the instructor's worksheet. Students should look at the large picture as the instructor reads each statement aloud. The method of answering is to complete each statement with an appropriate word. This skill incorporates good listening, comprehending, making inferences and associations and using these skills to retrieve an appropriate word. Answers may not always be the same but are correct if they complete an accurate statement.

1. The girl's hair is being blown by the _____.

2. She has her hands in her _____.

3. All the leaves have blown off the _____.

4. She is wearing a warm _____.

5. The jacket closes with a _____.

6. The girl is wearing shoes and _____.

7. Behind the clouds, I see the _____.

8. The warm weather has ended and now the days will be _____.

9. The leaves are being blown through the air by the _____.

10. If the girl did not have her hands in her pockets, they would be _____.

Name: _____

Date: _____

Language Development Lessons for
Early Childhood

Page 65

Great Ideas for Teaching, Inc.

Instructor's Worksheet

Yes or No Answers

DIRECTIONS: Before beginning, each student should be given a copy of the student worksheet that corresponds to the instructor's worksheet. Students should look at the large picture as the instructor reads each question aloud. The questions only require a <u>yes</u> or <u>no</u> answer. Some students may choose to verbalize more details. Non-verbal students may answer through their individual methods of indicating yes or no.

1. Are the boys fishing?

2. Are they fishing with tennis rackets?

3. Are they fishing in the ocean?

4. Are they standing on a pipe?

5. Will they get wet if they fall off the log?

6. Are the boys wearing shoes?

7. Do you see a frog in the picture?

8. Is the frog on a rock?

9. Do you see a fish in the picture?

10. Do you think it is a cold day?

Language Development Lessons for
Early Childhood

Instructor's Worksheet

Choosing Between Two Answers

<u>DIRECTIONS:</u> Before beginning, each student should be given a copy of the student worksheet that corresponds to the instructor's worksheet. Students should look at the large picture as the instructor reads each question aloud. Each question includes a choice of two answers. This method of questioning only requires recognizing the correct answer and repeating it. It is excellent practice for developing skills in answering questions.

1. Do you see two girls or two boys in the picture?

2. Are the boys fishing or painting?

3. Are they fishing with fishing poles or tennis rackets?

4. Are they fishing in the ocean or in a stream?

5. Are they on a pipe or a log?

6. Are the boys wearing pants or shorts?

7. If they fall off the log, will they stay dry or get wet?

8. Is the boy in the striped shirt standing or sitting on the log?

9. Do you see a fish or a snake jumping out of the water?

10. Is the frog sitting on a rock or a lily pad?

Language Development Lessons for
Early Childhood

Instructor's Worksheet   Completing Sentences

DIRECTIONS: Before beginning, each student should be given a copy of the student worksheet that corresponds to the instructor's worksheet. Students should look at the large picture as the instructor reads each statement aloud. The method of answering is to complete each statement with an appropriate word. This skill incorporates good listening, comprehending, making inferences and associations and using these skills to retrieve an appropriate word. Answers may not always be the same but are correct if they complete an accurate statement.

1. The boys are on a _____.

2. The log is over the _____.

3. The boys are _____.

4. They both have _____.

5. They each hope to catch a _____.

6. I see a frog on a _____.

7. If the boys fall, they will get _____.

8. They are barefooted because they took off their _____.

9. If the log slips, the boys will _____.

10. A fish is jumping out of the _____.

Name: _____

Date: _____

<u>DIRECTIONS:</u> Before beginning, each student should be given a copy of the student worksheet that corresponds to the instructor's worksheet. Students should look at the large picture as the instructor reads each question aloud. The questions only require a <u>yes</u> or <u>no</u> answer. Some students may choose to verbalize more details. Non-verbal students may answer through their individual methods of indicating yes or no.

1. Do you see a girl in the picture?

2. Does the little girl have black hair?

3. Does she have a bow in her hair?

4. Does the bow have polka-dots on it?

5. Does the girl have freckles on her face?

6. Do you see four flowers?

7. Are two flowers out of the ground?

8. Is the girl standing?

9. Is the girl holding a rake?

10. Is there a butterfly in the picture?

Instructor's Worksheet

Choosing Between Two Answers

<u>DIRECTIONS:</u> Before beginning, each student should be given a copy of the student worksheet that corresponds to the instructor's worksheet. Students should look at the large picture as the instructor reads each question aloud. Each question includes a choice of two answers. This method of questioning only requires recognizing the correct answer and repeating it. It is excellent practice for developing skills in answering questions.

1. Do you see a boy or a girl in the picture?

2. Does she have on a skirt or shorts?

3. Does she have buttons or a bow on her shirt?

4. Does she have a bow or a butterfly in her hair?

5. Does the bow have stripes or polka-dots on it?

6. Is she holding a flower or a balloon in her hand?

7. Is the girl standing up or kneeling?

8. Do you see the roots of all of the flowers or just one flower?

9. Is there a butterfly or a bee in the picture?

10. Does the little girl have freckles on her knees or on her face?

Language Development Lessons for
Early Childhood

Instructor's Worksheet   Completing Sentences

DIRECTIONS: Before beginning, each student should be given a copy of the student worksheet that corresponds to the instructor's worksheet. Students should look at the large picture as the instructor reads each statement aloud. The method of answering is to complete each statement with an appropriate word. This skill incorporates good listening, comprehending, making inferences and associations and using these skills to retrieve an appropriate word. Answers may not always be the same but are correct if they complete an accurate statement.

1. The girl dug up one _____.

2. The crooked pieces on the bottom of the stems are the _____.

3. Two flowers are still in the _____.

4. The insect flying above her is a _____.

5. A butterfly can fly because it has _____.

6. The girl is wearing a _____.

7. She is kneeling so we can't see her _____.

8. The insect walking on the ground is a _____.

9. A worm has no legs so it must _____.

10. The roots of the other two flowers are in the _____.

Name: _____

Instructor's Worksheet

Yes or No Answers

DIRECTIONS: Before beginning, each student should be given a copy of the student worksheet that corresponds to the instructor's worksheet. Students should look at the large picture as the instructor reads each question aloud. The questions only require a <u>yes</u> or <u>no</u> answer. Some students may choose to verbalize more details. Non-verbal students may answer through their individual methods of indicating yes or no.

1. Do you see a girl in the picture?

2. Does she have a friend with her?

3. Is she sitting in a chair?

4. Is she painting a picture?

5. Is she holding a tray of cookies?

6. Is she holding more than one paintbrush?

7. Is the girl wearing a painting apron?

8. Does her apron have straps?

9. Is she painting outside by a swimming pool?

10. Is the frame that is holding the picture called an easel?

Instructor's Worksheet   Choosing Between Two Answers

DIRECTIONS: Before beginning, each student should be given a copy of the student worksheet that corresponds to the instructor's worksheet. Students should look at the large picture as the instructor reads each question aloud. Each question includes a choice of two answers. This method of questioning only requires recognizing the correct answer and repeating it. It is excellent practice for developing skills in answering questions.

1. Do you see a boy or a girl in the picture?

2. Is she a big girl or a little girl?

3. Does she have dark hair or light hair?

4. Is she sitting or standing?

5. Is she holding a paintbrush or a hairbrush?

6. Is she painting or erasing?

7. Does the paint palette have one color or different color paints?

8. Is the girl painting a picture of apples or flowers?

9. Is she wearing boots or shoes?

10. Is the frame she is using called an easel or a ladder?

<u>DIRECTIONS:</u> Before beginning, each student should be given a copy of the student worksheet that corresponds to the instructor's worksheet. Students should look at the large picture as the instructor reads each statement aloud. The method of answering is to complete each statement with an appropriate word. This skill incorporates good listening, comprehending, making inferences and associations and using these skills to retrieve an appropriate word. Answers may not always be the same but are correct if they complete an accurate statement.

1. The girl is painting _____.

2. She is painting with a _____.

3. She is holding a palette with five colors of _____.

4. Her picture is propped up on the _____.

5. I know she is a happy because she is _____.

6. The extra brushes and paints are on the _____.

7. The girl has dark, curly _____.

8. She is wearing an apron over her _____.

9. She has not finished painting the _____.

10. She likes to stand when she is _____.

Name: _____

Date: _____

Instructor's Worksheet

Yes or No Answers

DIRECTIONS: Before beginning, each student should be given a copy of the student worksheet that corresponds to the instructor's worksheet. Students should look at the large picture as the instructor reads each question aloud. The questions only require a <u>yes</u> or <u>no</u> answer. Some students may choose to verbalize more details. Non-verbal students may answer through their individual methods of indicating yes or no.

1. Is the boy riding his bike on the driveway?

2. Is the garage door closed?

3. Does the garage door have windows?

4. Is the dog holding some letters?

5. Is the boy riding a tricycle?

6. Is the dog's tail wagging?

7. Does the picture look like wintertime?

8. Is the dog standing in the driveway?

9. Is there a car in the driveway?

10. Do you think the boys are waiting for the school bus?

Instructor's Worksheet

Choosing Between Two Answers

DIRECTIONS: Before beginning, each student should be given a copy of the student worksheet that corresponds to the instructor's worksheet. Students should look at the large picture as the instructor reads each question aloud. Each question includes a choice of two answers. This method of questioning only requires recognizing the correct answer and repeating it. It is excellent practice for developing skills in answering questions.

1. Is the boy riding his bicycle on the driveway or on the road?

2. Is the garage door open or closed?

3. Is the dog holding letters or dog biscuits in its mouth?

4. Is the mailbox open or closed?

5. Is the boy riding a bicycle or a tricycle?

6. Do the boys have on shorts or long pants?

7. Do the boys have on long-sleeved or short-sleeved shirts?

8. Is the dog standing in the road or on the driveway?

9. Are there three windows or two windows in the garage?

10. Who delivered the mail, a mailman or a fireman?

Instructor's Worksheet

Completing Sentences

DIRECTIONS: Before beginning, each student should be given a copy of the student worksheet that corresponds to the instructor's worksheet. Students should look at the large picture as the instructor reads each statement aloud. The method of answering is to complete each statement with an appropriate word. This skill incorporates good listening, comprehending, making inferences and associations and using these skills to retrieve an appropriate word. Answers may not always be the same but are correct if they complete an accurate statement.

1. One boy is riding a _____.

2. The garage door has three _____.

3. It is summer so the tree has _____.

4. The boy's bicycle has two _____.

5. The dog is standing on the _____.

6. The person who delivers mail is called a _____.

7. At night, their mom parks her car in the _____.

8. The boy on the bike is holding on to the _____.

9. The postman put the mail in the _____.

10. The dog's tail is _____.